Terminal Illness

 caring for yourself and others

PASTORAL · OUTREACH · SERIES ·

Terminal Illness

caring for yourself and others

Dr Elizabeth Toy,
Dr Catherine O'Neill
and Dr Sarah Jackson

redemptorist
publications

Published by Redemptorist Publications
Alphonsus House, Chawton, Hampshire, GU34 3HQ, UK
Tel: +44 (0)1420 88222, Fax: +44 (0)1420 88805
Email: rp@rpbooks.co.uk, www.rpbooks.co.uk

A registered charity limited by guarantee
Registered in England 3261721

Series Editor: Sister Janet Fearns
Edited by Mandy Woods
Designed by Eliana Thompson

ISBN 978-0-85231-521-7

The publisher gratefully acknowledges permission to use the following copyright material:

Excerpts from the *New Revised Standard Version Bible: Anglicised Edition*, copyright © 1989,
1995, Division of Christian Education of the National Council of the Churches of Christ in
the United States of America. Used by permission. All rights reserved.

'Prayer for Inner Peace and Strength' by Julie Palmer, © 2018 Capernaum Publishing.

St Augustine, *Confessions*, as quoted in *After Death: Life in God*, by Norman Pittinger
(New York: Seabury Press, 1980).

Hope and Grace, Monika Renz (London: Jessica Kingsley Publishers, 2016).

The Heart and Mind of Mary Ward, Anthony Clarke (Wheathampstead: Anthony Clarke Books, 1985).

Thanks to Alizoun Dickinson for the information regarding end-of-life doulas and to
Maggie Draper, Head of Supportive Care at Hospiscare, for the information regarding bereavement.

Every effort has been made to trace copyright holders and to obtain their permission for the
use of copyright material. The publisher apologises for any errors or omissions and would
be grateful for notification of any corrections that should be incorporated in future reprints
or editions of this book.

Printed by Lithgo Press Ltd.,
Leicester, LE8 6NU

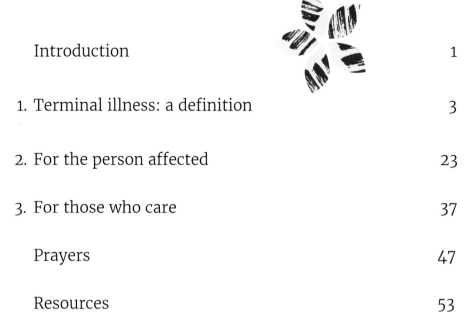

Introduction

Terminal illness: the challenge

In the Western world, advances in medicine leading to, for example, vaccination and the use of powerful antibiotics, have eradicated many of the causes of early death. It is rare that we imagine our own or a loved one's ending, but if we do, in our mind it is often due to an unnatural cause.

In recent times, illness and death have become removed from normal family life and medicalised. Relatively few people under the age of sixty have witnessed death. Perception of what illness and dying is like is often shaped by film and television. More often than not, that perception is frightening, whereas the reality should be anything but.

In this book we hope to share some insights into the challenges associated with terminal or "life-limiting" illness. We would also like to provide reassurance that help and support is available to ensure that life with a terminal condition can be lived to the full and that when the end of life comes, this can be a grace-filled, dignified and peaceful experience.

1

Terminal illness: a definition

What is meant by the phrase "terminal illness"?

Strictly speaking, a terminal illness is one that cannot be cured and that may shorten life expectancy. It is unlikely that this terminology will be used by medical staff when discussing a progressive and incurable condition, although patients themselves frequently ask, "Is it terminal?"

More commonly, a terminal condition is referred to as a life-limiting condition. Such conditions include cancers and chronic diseases affecting major organs, such as the heart, lungs, kidneys and brain. Prognoses in such conditions may vary from days to many years depending on the condition.

People often hear the word cancer and make assumptions that death is imminent, yet more people today are living with or beyond cancer than ever before due to advances in medicine. The same is true of other non-malignant conditions.

Receiving a diagnosis of a terminal condition

For many, receiving the diagnosis of a terminal or life-limiting condition can be an overwhelming, devastating and very frightening experience. For some, the diagnosis may be completely unexpected. For others, there may be a sense of relief that now there is some explanation for the way they have been feeling or the symptoms they have been experiencing.

At the time of diagnosis, you should be given opportunities to ask questions and access support. In many cases you will be introduced to a healthcare professional, often a clinical nurse specialist, who will act as your "key-worker". This person will be your main point of contact, with whom you can build an ongoing and trusting relationship. Your key-worker will provide you and those close to you with ongoing information and support and will act as the link between you and all the healthcare professionals involved in your care.

It is important that you have confidence in the team looking after you. In the National Health Service (NHS) today, most serious diagnoses such as cancer or motor neurone disease will be discussed by a multidisciplinary team of experts in that disease area. This team will generally include specialist doctors, radiologists, pathologists, clinical nurse specialists and professionals allied to medicine such as dietitians and physiotherapists. They will review all the available information about your condition and make a holistic suggestion of treatment (that is, including medicines, medical interventions or physical therapies) to your lead consultant.

Seeking a second opinion

The team looking after you will discuss appropriate treatments for your condition. This may include types of treatment not routinely funded by the NHS.

Sometimes you may be offered the option of "topping up" the treatment and paying the excess treatment costs yourself.

If you are genuinely concerned that the medical advice being offered is incorrect or suboptimal you are at liberty to ask your GP to refer you to another specialist for a second opinion.

Most hospital specialists will not be offended by this and would prefer that you are comfortable with your treatment decision. It is wise, however, to ask for their advice on whom that second opinion should come from as they will be aware of other experts in your condition.

Treatment, side effects and symptoms

Specific treatments will depend on the individual condition. For those people with a diagnosis of cancer, treatments may include surgery, radiotherapy, chemotherapy or other drug treatments. For those with life-limiting conditions other than cancer, there may also be a wide variety of treatment options available. Although the aim is to delay the progression of the underlying disease and/or improve its symptoms, this is sadly not always achievable and the management plan may need to be adapted appropriately.

Although most medical treatments will be associated with some side effects, such as fatigue, nausea and vomiting, constipation or pain, these are usually manageable with appropriate advice and support.

If, however, you feel the burden of treatment outweighs the benefits it is important to raise this with your family and the medical team caring for you. Similarly, the medical team may advise that continuing therapy will do more harm than good.

When enough is enough

Personal story...

Kaye was a ninety-three-year-old retired teacher. She had multiple medical problems but the most recent issues she faced were profound tiredness, breathlessness and reduced mobility related to significant leg swelling. She was found to have a heart murmur. An ultrasound of the heart demonstrated a leaky aortic valve and very poor heart function. She had already had several admissions to hospital with breathlessness. Each time she had a drip inserted for powerful medicines and oxygen for several days.

During her last admission to the cardiology ward Kaye had felt fed up of blood tests and spending time in hospital. She had an open and frank discussion with the junior doctor on the ward. Kaye understood that her prognosis was just a few months. She wanted to be at home alongside her elderly husband, to be able to see her garden and to be visited by her young great-grandson.

She was referred to the palliative care team. Her bed was brought downstairs. Home oxygen was arranged. Her medication regimen was simplified such that non-essential tablets were stopped but those that helped alleviate her symptoms were continued.

A care plan was completed reflecting her wishes. Care at home was organised with support from both the community heart failure team and the palliative care team. Kaye took the opportunity to see the hospital chaplain prior to her discharge from hospital. A few weeks later she died peacefully in the living room at home, surrounded by her family, and with a panoramic view of her garden.

The multidisciplinary team

Throughout the course of your illness, you will meet and be supported by a whole team of professionals. This is the multidisciplinary team (MDT). Though the members of the team will possess a variety of different roles and skills, they will all share the common aim of guiding and supporting you through your journey. The MDT will likely include specialist doctors and nurses. An occupational therapist will help you to live as independently as possible for as long as possible, taking a key role in organising and facilitating safe discharge from hospital and care at home. A physiotherapist can help with mobility, the provision of mobility aids and optimising your physical abilities.

At some point, you may meet the palliative care team who specialise in the symptomatic management of people with life-limiting conditions, aiming to improve their quality of life. Social workers are pivotal in assisting with the provision of care and practical and financial advice. Other team members may include psychological support specialists, complementary therapists and spiritual care professionals.

Ongoing care

You may need to attend the hospital outpatient department regularly to see your specialist doctor or nurse and this may prove tiring and challenging. Investigate the easiest and most reliable transport and avoid hospital parking if possible. Sometimes clinics run late, so take along a good book. Students may be present in clinic, though there is no obligation for you to see them.

You may also need to attend the day care unit for blood tests, investigations or a blood transfusion. Occasionally patients are admitted to hospital for more rapid access to tests or for symptom control.

Wards can be busy and noisy places to be and the team looking after you will endeavour to get you home as soon as possible. Each ward will have specific visiting hours. If you are fatigued, try to limit the number of visitors you have or to space them out.

Preparation for a clinic appointment

To get the most out of any appointments you attend, it is important to do some preparation. Think about whom you might want to take with you to the appointment.

Too many people can be a distraction, and ideally it would be best to arrange childcare if you have young children. Consider taking along a trusted friend or family member.

Write a list of questions before you see the doctor or a member of your team. You may need to make contact with your team in between clinic appointments, so ensure you have the contact details for your consultant's secretary or for your specialist nurse.

Try to always bring along an up-to-date copy of your medication list.

Other questions you may have for your healthcare team

1. Genetics

Genetic inheritance: "Is this something I could have passed on to my children?" is a common question that occurs when someone is diagnosed with a serious illness.

While obviously every case is different, as a general rule, inherited conditions usually occur at an early age. In order to give a more accurate answer your doctor may take a family history, looking for potentially linked conditions, and may possibly refer you to a specialist clinical genetics team. If appropriate they may suggest some specific DNA testing to give you a definitive answer.

Some conditions do not yet have a definite genetic mutation identified. In such cases you may be invited to join a clinical study or to store some blood in a tissue bank for testing in the future should new evidence become available.

2. Organ donation

Depending on your illness, the organs you are able to donate for transplantation may be restricted. Do make sure that your family are aware of your wishes as you may find that medical staff are occasionally unwilling to raise the question at the time of your death for fear of adding to people's distress. This is something you may wish to include in an advance care plan (see p. 14).

3. Clinical trials

It is important to appreciate that clinical trials are indeed trials and are not a guarantee of a superior treatment.

Many trials will compare a promising new therapy with the existing gold-standard therapy or technique. Although these new treatments have potential for improving either quality or length of life, it is equally possible they may either show no difference or lead to a worse outcome.

It is important to weigh up the potential benefits and downsides of taking part in a clinical trial. While participating in one often results in close monitoring, additional scans and the knowledge that others in the future may benefit, this may be at the personal cost of additional time spent in hospital and travelling when family time is important. Very early phase studies may be even more altruistic as they may simply be exploring a safe and effective dose of a drug rather than being expected to make an improvement in your condition.

4. Holidays

Holidays can be an important opportunity to spend quality time with friends and family. Although your illness may place some limitations on your plans, it does not necessarily mean they should all be put on hold.

Having accurate information about your short-term prognosis is important. Is a rapid deterioration likely? If you decide to go abroad, do make sure that your insurance is valid and comprehensive. Failing to disclose something that you do not think could be deemed related may not be interpreted that way by an insurance company.

Although you may think that if you become unwell you will simply book the next flight home, you should consider the potential costs of medical repatriation should you be deemed unfit to travel.

Sometimes one insurer can quote a very high premium while another may be far more reasonable – so do shop around.

You should also consider letting your healthcare team know of your holiday plans. You may need additional advice from them concerning subjects such as travelling with certain drugs (for example, strong painkillers) and essential documents you may need to take with you.

Information and resources

The internet can be a valuable source of information. However, it can also be confusing or misleading. Information from national charities such as Cancer Research UK, Macmillan and Parkinson's UK will generally be accurate as they engage medical experts to review all published materials.

Likewise, many professional bodies have public web pages which give helpful guidance (for example, Hospice UK, https://www.hospiceuk.org/; Royal College of Radiologists, https://www.rcr.ac.uk/; British Geriatric Society, http://www.bgs.org.uk/). Be wary of anecdotes, however – while these are generally well-meaning, the advice given may be misleading or detrimental to your own condition. The NHS Choices website (www.nhs.uk) maintains an updated list of organisations which may be useful.

Patient support groups can be a valuable resource. These often meet in community centres or venues run by charitable organisations. They provide an opportunity for you to meet people who either have been diagnosed with a similar condition themselves or have been a carer for someone. Although everyone's illness is unique, such groups are often described as an opportunity to meet others who speak your language through shared experience.

Other sources of support

1. Charitable organisations
There are a number of organisations that are able to provide small grants – for example, for a piece of equipment. Others offer holiday opportunities for families to spend quality time together.

2. Personal health budgets
Personal health budgets are a relatively new initiative whereby you are given a budget to employ others to help you with your needs. This may be used to pay for professional care or to reimburse a family member or friend who can help you. As you know your needs and preferences best, this can often provide a good means of ensuring flexible and personalised care.

3. Community palliative care
Marie Curie (www.mariecurie.org.uk) can often provide night sitters for one or two nights per week to enable your family members to get some rest, with the reassurance that you are being looked after. In most areas specialist supportive and palliative care teams linked to your acute hospital, local hospice and general practitioner will provide expert advice regarding symptom control to you at home.

4. Respite care
Respite care is available in some specialist residential and nursing homes. Occasionally they may provide themed weeks – for example, craft weeks where people who have significant care needs and yet share a common interest are able to come together with a group of like-minded people.

5. End-of-life doulas
A "doula" is a non-medical person who acts as a supporter at a time when an individual and their family most need the informed and compassionate presence of someone who is prepared to "walk with them".

End-of-life doulas support people with life-limiting illnesses and those they love. They are a consistent and flexible, non-medicalised presence working alongside health and social care professionals to fill in the gaps.

A doula will provide practical care and support (in a person's home, hospital, hospice or care home) to achieve an atmosphere of peace and normality. They will also take the time to sit with the dying person and simply be present.

The dying person is placed at the centre and is supported holistically – practically, physically, emotionally and spiritually.

The relationship may begin from the time of diagnosis or in later stages, and the doula often continues to support the loved ones after the person's death.

Some choose to volunteer, while others work and charge professionally.

Doulas also work in their communities to inform and educate people and to facilitate them to take ownership and feel confident to care for a person at the end of their life.

Living Well Dying Well (www.lwdwtraining.uk) is the leading training and networking organisation for end-of-life doulas in the UK.

Discussing prognosis

A member of the healthcare team involved in your care should offer you the opportunity to ask questions about the future, including discussing your likely prognosis (that is, the course your illness is likely to take and possible life expectancy). Please feel free to raise questions about prognosis with your healthcare team at any time. There is no obligation to have these discussions and they should take place when you feel the time is right for you.

The opportunities to discuss prognosis may present themselves at different points along your journey with a life-limiting condition. However, questions around prognosis may become more prominent as you begin to approach the end of your life.

Prognosis can be very difficult to predict and any attempts at giving a prognosis are at best a well-informed guess. However, having some idea about possible timescales can be helpful in terms of being able to plan and prioritise for the future.

For patients with advanced cancer who are no longer receiving anti-cancer treatment, but who are receiving best supportive or palliative care (see below), the prognosis may be more predictable. In these patients, there is often a steady decline in their overall functioning which can guide prognosis. So, for example, if someone appears to be deteriorating from month to month, prognosis may be measured in months. If the observed deterioration is occurring on a weekly basis, the prognosis may be weeks. Once someone is seen to be deteriorating on a daily basis, the prognosis may be very short – just hours to days.

In life-limiting conditions, such as heart failure, renal failure, chronic respiratory diseases or neurodegenerative conditions, prognosis can be even more difficult to estimate due to the fluctuating nature of these conditions. Someone may experience an acute deterioration which may necessitate hospital admission and treatment, but they may recover from it, though perhaps at a lower rate of wellness than they were before the deterioration. This makes estimating prognosis very challenging.

Indicators that may suggest a shorter prognosis include: recurrent or more frequent hospital admissions; worsening symptoms; loss of appetite or weight; declining mobility; increasing problems with swallowing or speech; and recurrent chest infections.

Sudden and unexpected events, such as blood clots, overwhelming infections or significant bleeding, can occur which may bring about death sooner than had been anticipated. It may or may not be appropriate to actively treat such events, depending on how unwell the person was prior to the event and what their previous wishes were and are. The healthcare professionals involved in your care or in the care of someone close to you will do their best to anticipate such events; to prepare you for them and to ascertain your wishes around levels of care.

Disease progression and the role of supportive and palliative care

Following the diagnosis of a potentially life-limiting condition, it is likely that the patient, and those close to him or her, may need some form of specialist supportive care.

This is usually provided by supportive and palliative care teams and aims to help patients and their families cope with the condition and its treatment, from the point of diagnosis to the point of deterioration and death and into bereavement.

At some point following the diagnosis of a life-limiting illness, the condition will progress. The point at which this happens is variable, depending on the individual, the condition and the response to treatment. It may be within days, weeks, months or years of the initial diagnosis. The focus may then start to shift away from extending life and more towards optimising quality of life by providing good symptom control and offering psychosocial and spiritual support to both the individual and those close to him or her.

End-of-life care

End-of-life care often refers to care given to people in the final hours or days of their lives. More broadly, end-of-life care may refer to the care given to those with a terminal or life-limiting condition that has become advanced, progressive and incurable.

The provision of good end-of-life care is a shared responsibility between healthcare teams across all settings, the person's family and members of the wider community.

End-of-life care includes the practical and technical delivery of care to the individual who is dying. It also includes the provision of practical support and information such as financial advice and bereavement care both to the dying person and to the people who are important to them.

Preparing for the future: advance care planning, advance statements and advance decisions

If you have a life-limiting condition or are approaching the end of life, or if this is the situation for someone close to you, it may be important to start thinking about and planning for your future care. This process is sometimes called "advance care planning".

Planning ahead allows you to inform others (family, carers, healthcare professionals) of your wishes and feelings while you are still able to do so. It aims to increase the likelihood of you receiving the care you want, in the place you desire, at the point you become more unwell or unable to make decisions for yourself. You may also wish to consider sharing information about desired funeral arrangements, including any specific cultural, spiritual or religious needs that you would wish to be respected or any other practical matters. It may be important to consider anything you would not want to happen to you (for example, admission to hospital) or any wishes around organ donation. This can be formally documented as an Advance Statement. Although not legally binding, an Advance Statement should be taken into account by the healthcare professionals involved in your care.

Planning ahead can help address some of the worries or questions that may be on your mind. It can often be a very positive experience, as once they have been addressed you can get on with living as well as you can for as long as you can. Family and friends will also be more confident in knowing exactly what you do and don't want to happen.

Advance decision to refuse treatment

An advance decision to refuse treatment (or ADRT) differs from an Advance Statement, in that it is a formal, legally binding document. It allows individuals to refuse certain treatments, in the event that they are unable to speak for themselves.

It is possible for you to decide in advance which treatments you would not wish to receive at the end of your life. This may include treatments such as antibiotics, artificial fluids (via a drip), artificial nutrition (via feeding tubes or drips), breathing support (including different types of breathing masks and tubes), kidney dialysis, circulatory support (drugs that support the heart) and cardio-pulmonary resuscitation (CPR).

Generally, in someone with an advanced, life-limiting condition, in whom prognosis is poor, invasive treatments such as CPR may be neither successful nor appropriate. CPR has a very low chance of success in patients close to the end of their life, and may cause significant trauma as well as potentially compromising a person's dignity.

For this reason, CPR is rarely offered as a treatment to patients nearing the end of their life. Your healthcare professional should discuss this with you and document that you would not be suitable to receive such treatment on a "Do Not Attempt Cardio-Pulmonary Resuscitation" (DNACPR) form.

You should be given a copy of this form to share with all involved in your care. Equally, if you already know that you would not wish to receive this treatment, it is important to raise the issue with your medical team to ensure your wishes are respected.

A DNACPR decision does not preclude someone from receiving other forms of treatment, such as fluids or antibiotics. It may be helpful to discuss with your healthcare provider which treatments you would be prepared to receive and under what circumstances. Sometimes these decisions will be documented in such a way that the information is readily accessible to all the healthcare professionals involved in your care – for example, on a ReSPECT (Recommended Summary Plan for Emergency Care and Treatment) form or a TEP (Treatment Escalation Plan) form.

Lasting power of attorney for health and welfare

When considering the future, you may decide that you would like someone to be able to speak and make decisions on your behalf. This may be a relative, a friend or a professional. A lasting power of attorney, or LPA, is a legal means of giving this person the authority to do so.

There are two forms of LPA.

The first covers *property and financial affairs.*

The second allows a person to make decisions about your *health and welfare.*

A health and welfare LPA may be used to give the attorney the power to make decisions about where you should live, about day-to-day care, and about consenting to or refusing medical care, although an attorney can only consent to or refuse treatment if they are given the specific authority to do this in the LPA.

An LPA application must be registered with the Office of the Public Guardian before it is valid.

Nutrition and hydration at the end of life

Progressive loss of appetite and the consequent reduction in oral intake is a common manifestation of disease progression in all life-limiting conditions.

Increasing fatigue can suppress appetite and consequently a person's desire to eat, as can some medications, and it can also be an effect of the disease itself. This can be frustrating for the affected person and for those close to them. However, at this time in someone's illness, the body is no longer able to utilise the nutrients from food, and the effort of trying to eat can be too great. Food should be viewed more as being for pleasure, rather than as a necessity.

It is important to offer food that a person may fancy, while avoiding placing them under any unnecessary pressure to eat.

There is sometimes a danger that repeated offering can be counterproductive and can lead to meals being a tense and difficult experience. For the person suffering, feeling pressured to eat often leads to feelings of nausea and anxiety, while the healthy members of the family feel guilty about eating in front of them. It can sometimes be helpful to offer a small portion on a smaller plate, as this may look less overwhelming. Another idea is to simply have just one course of the meal together.

If someone in the last hours and days of their life stops drinking or is too sleepy to swallow, their mouth may look dry. This does not always mean they are dehydrated or even thirsty.

It is normal for all dying people eventually to stop eating and drinking. To administer artificial nutrition or fluid to a dying person could risk causing more harm. They would require the insertion of a needle into the vein which, for the dying person, can be painful or distressing.

Also, because the body of a dying person is no longer able to utilise nutrition or fluids in the usual way, administration of such products can lead to problems with vomiting and fluid accumulation, causing breathing difficulties, excessive respiratory secretions and abdominal and leg swelling. There may be occasions, however, when fluids are administered subcutaneously for the person's comfort.

If the dying person has moments of consciousness and they ask for something to eat or drink, sips of fluid or small amounts of soft foods (for example, ice cream or sorbet) may be offered. Sips of fluid through a straw (or from a teaspoon or syringe), moistening the mouth with a damp sponge, placing ice chips in the mouth or applying lip balm can also bring great comfort.

End of life: what is dying like?

A commonly asked question from both those with a life-limiting condition and those close to them is what will dying be like?

Many people imagine and worry that death will be a very painful or distressing process. Some are fearful of experiencing other difficult symptoms at the end of life such as severe breathlessness, vomiting or agitation.

In reality, and for the most part, the dying process is a gradual, gentle and peaceful process, whereby a person deteriorates over a period of hours or a short number of days.

Over this time, they may become weaker and may take to bed, spending increasing amounts of time resting and sleeping, and eating and drinking less.

Eventually, the dying person will become unrousable and unable to communicate or take food or fluids by mouth, though there may be still some awareness of familiar voices and surroundings.

Bodily functions may gradually decline and cease, including the passage of urine and faeces. There may be changes in skin colour and skin may become cool to the touch.

As death approaches, there may be changes to a person's breathing, with speeding up or slowing down of the breathing rate, more shallow breathing or pauses in the breathing pattern.

The breathing may also sound more noisy or bubbly. This occurs because of a pooling of normal salivary secretions at the back of the throat. As someone becomes more deeply unconscious, they become less able to clear these secretions. While this can be distressing to those observing, it is usually not felt to be distressing to the dying person. Medications are available to reduce secretions if they are causing the dying person distress.

As death occurs, breathing stops, followed by the heart. Occasionally there may be some additional efforts at breathing which may last several minutes. This is not distressing to the patient but can be alarming to witness. Death will be confirmed by a clinician.

End of life: managing symptoms

A syringe pump or syringe driver is a plastic syringe contained within a small battery-driven pump. It is attached to a short plastic line and needle, which is inserted just beneath the skin. The device is very small (about the size of a small lunchbox) and can be placed underneath a pillow. The syringe can contain several medications simultaneously, which can be delivered to patients gradually over the course of a twenty-four-hour period.

Increasingly, syringe pumps are being used earlier in the course of an illness, to try and improve the person's symptoms. An example would be someone who was vomiting and therefore unable to manage their oral tablets. At some point in the future, it may then be appropriate to stop the syringe pump and return to taking oral medications.

However, as someone enters the final days and hours of life, they may become progressively more sleepy and unable to take their usual medications by mouth. This may be an appropriate time for the healthcare professionals to review which medications are essential to continue and which could be stopped. Essential medications include those that alleviate symptoms, such as painkillers or anti-sickness medications. These can be administered via the syringe pump. This ensures that there is a constant and reliable administration of medication over a twenty-four-hour period and avoids the risk of someone "missing" an important medication.

Syringe pumps can be used in any setting, including in a person's own home. The medications need to be renewed every twenty-four hours. This is usually facilitated by the local district nursing team or by the ward-based team. The use of a syringe pump does not hasten a person's death. However, the need for a syringe pump often reflects someone's deteriorating condition.

After the death has been confirmed, the body is usually washed and prepared before being taken to a mortuary or funeral home. A death certificate and, if required, a cremation form will be issued by a doctor.

Occasionally, the medical team may need to discuss the death with the coroner's office before issuing a certificate to ensure that a post-mortem is not required. One may be needed if the cause of death is unclear, even in the context of a known illness; other reasons for a post-mortem include if there has been recent surgery or if the illness may have been contributed to by any previous employment. The death needs to be registered before funeral arrangements can be confirmed.

Many employers offer a period of compassionate leave to close relatives after bereavement in recognition of the loss they have suffered.

The death of a loved one is an experience that we will all have to face in our lives, and to mourn someone deeply is entirely normal. Each of us experiences grief in our own particular way. People of different cultures, beliefs and ages will have different ways of mourning and of supporting one another.

If you have been expecting a death over days and weeks, you may feel a mixture of emotions: sadness, relief, or numbness and an inability to believe that it has finally happened. Bereaved people often have physical symptoms such as a stomach pain, or experience anxiety and find it difficult to concentrate. They may be exhausted from their caring role, which has abruptly come to an end.

Mourning is also exhausting, and people sometimes struggle with making decisions or plans and can feel overwhelmed. It is important therefore to try not to make any important decision too soon after a loss.

If the death is sudden, or feels sudden, the people left can be very shocked and angry. People who are grieving can be angry with their family, with God, with health professionals or even with the person who has died, for leaving them behind. It is good to be aware of this, as it is sad when family members are angry with each other, just when they most need support.

Often conflict over funeral arrangements or wills is because of misplaced anger and guilt. People can constantly replay the last days and weeks, wanting a different end to the story and feeling guilty perhaps that they did not say everything they wanted to say, or questioning whether they made the right decisions.

For people of faith, many find the rituals, practices and beliefs of their faith very supportive at this time – but the death of a loved one can also challenge these beliefs and people can feel forsaken and isolated, and angry with God.

In the early days of bereavement, grief can be experienced in sharp and intense waves, overlain by a constant sense of loss. There are constant daily reminders of the loss: when you go shopping, or lay the table, or go home to an empty house. People can suffer from depression and feel hopeless as they contemplate a different future from the one that they had planned. Bereaved people describe having good days, and then suddenly feeling overwhelmed by their loss.

We know that bereavement is not a smooth journey but instead is full of ups and downs.

Living with a loss becomes easier over time: we do not forget the person who has died and we still feel their loss acutely, but we learn to live without them. We weave a new future, and their influence and the things that they taught us or that we shared are woven into that future. It is in our memories that the ones we love live on and remain part of our lives, as we remember a word, a deed, a touch or a smile, a way of looking at the world, or a characteristic way of doing things.

A great man of the early Church, St Augustine, wrote this in Book Four of his *Confessions*, about the loss of one we love:

> "We can never lose those whom we have loved, if we have loved them in God, since we have loved them in the God whom we can never lose."

2

For the person affected

Adjusting to the diagnosis

Being diagnosed with a life-limiting condition will initially affect us all in different ways as we have our own characters and coping mechanisms. Many of these responses will be shaped by past experience and our inbuilt ideas of how we should respond.

However, as time goes on, there are a number of emotional and psychological responses to significant bad news that are commonly seen, regardless of one's background or underlying illness.

These have been described by many authors and researchers who have worked extensively in palliative care environments. Maybe the best known of these professionals is Elisabeth Kübler-Ross. In her book *On Death and Dying* she describes five stages that people will experience: denial and isolation; anger; bargaining; depression; and acceptance.

However, this is often not a linear journey, as is recognised by Swiss psycho-oncologist Monika Renz, who describes a four-stage model of maturation. In this she recognises that living with a life-limiting illness is a continual back-and-forth process, with people, both patients and their loved ones, struggling through the emotional cycle over and over again. One of the important messages within this is that during the period of illness, the inner being continues to grow, spiritually and emotionally, even if the physical exterior appears to be shrinking.

In her book *Hope and Grace*, Monika Renz describes the gradual alteration of "What may I hope for?"

> "From the hope of getting well to the hope of experiencing good times again.
> From the hope of living to the hope of dying well.
> From the hope for oneself to a hope beyond oneself."

Hope is vital for our human existence. It is what motivates us whatever our given situation, however difficult it might be.

The first time we hear a formal diagnosis or are given a prognosis, it is common to think: "This can't be right. This cannot be happening to me."

Although at the back of our minds we know that something is not right and intellectually understand the process of medical investigation, it is often only when the words are spoken out loud that the significance of the news is recognised. It will challenge our understanding of the meaning of our life and throw plans for our future into disarray.

Worried about what the doctors might find

Personal story...

Lewis was a seventy-eight-year-old retired magician who had enjoyed smoking since his youth. A consultant specialising in healthcare for older people had been asked to see him in his own home because he had deteriorated significantly. He had lost three stone in weight, was housebound and had started to fall. His home was cluttered and it was evident that he was unable to manage at home.

Lewis refused to be admitted to hospital because he was frightened and fearful of what the doctors might find, although he agreed to some outpatient investigations.

While he was awaiting tests he became weaker and reluctantly agreed to be admitted to the acute hospital. He was struggling to swallow. He was found to have metastatic cancer of the throat. Lewis was offered palliative chemotherapy but declined any treatment that might extend his life. He did not have any family. His main concern was his parrot "Bobo".

The nursing staff ensured the parrot would be looked after in the long term by making contact with the RSPCA. The palliative care team were involved in Lewis's care and identified that he wished to be cared for in his own home.

Lewis deteriorated faster than anticipated but the palliative care team, alongside social services, managed to coordinate a round-the-clock plan for carers and night sitters along with support from the community nursing teams. Lewis's bed was moved downstairs. He returned home for the last nine days of his life to enjoy the company of Bobo. Lewis experienced a great sense of relief at being in familiar surroundings.

Focus on life

Frequently the news comes as a huge shock. Much of the rest of the consultation will not be heard as we try to process it. Sometimes we will go into autopilot and ask questions. One of the first questions that often comes to mind is, "How will I die?" often followed by, "When will that be?"

These questions may or may not be answered fully at that time and the initial few hours and days may feel like a blur, maybe even like looking in from the outside on a world that is no longer our own.

While the prognosis will vary from person to person, in some cases being just short weeks and for others, many years, within the time that is left, it is important to maintain a focus on living, as well as on the prospect of dying.

Work and relationships

The importance of living is often centred around our relationships and the roles we play. These are what give our lives meaning. We may be a father, a daughter, the football coach or the school dinner lady. All of these roles and responsibilities bring us a sense of worth; our service to others brings its own reward.

Depending on their age as well as on other circumstances, many people will be working in either paid or voluntary roles when they become ill. A diagnosis of a life-limiting illness does not necessarily mean that these roles must be relinquished immediately.

Many employers will be flexible around working patterns and duties. Being able to stay in employment can be valuable, not simply in terms of financial benefit, but also for companionship and the opportunity for the focus to be on your job rather than on the illness.

For those unable to continue working, there are various financial options depending on the contract under which they were employed and the length of service. It is best to take formal financial advice. Organisations such as the Citizens Advice Bureau can often point you in the right direction. Some people will be entitled to sick pay, while others will be able to retire early on grounds of ill health. Mortgages and insurance policies often include cover for the "diagnosis of a terminal illness", which, for these purposes, is often defined as a prognosis of less than twelve months. There are also a number of state benefits and grants which may help financially. Take your time to evaluate the best options: there is often no immediate rush.

Making preparations

Depending on the nature of the illness, there may be a need to prepare to hand on some of the family and voluntary responsibilities. This can be harder than it seems, in view of the emotional commitment we make. It can sometimes feel like a bereavement letting go of that role and you may grieve its loss. Again, take time.

Although you are ill, there are many things you will be able to do, even if they take a little longer or you need help from others. You will also derive pleasure from doing them and handing on your wisdom and experience.

You will probably hear many references in the media and from friends to "fighting the disease" and "not letting it beat you". The difficulty when facing a life-limiting illness is that ultimately, despite all one's best efforts, the illness will begin to take its toll and the person suffering from the illness will begin to become weaker.

It can be better to "hope for the best but prepare for the worst". Some people find it easier to think of the concept of living alongside the illness or disease. In accepting that it will never go away, the emphasis switches to accommodating the illness and lack of certainty which accompanies it, to establishing a "new normal", and to living in the moment.

In this way, rather than wasting energy and time searching for the "magic bullet" or trying to continue the appearance of normality to the outside world, time is given to relationships, things and events that give pleasure. It has been said often that when someone is given the bad news of a serious illness, their senses recalibrate to appreciate the simple things in life.

Quality of life at the end of life

Bob was an eighty-six-year-old ex-pilot with increasing frailty, recurrent falls and progressive dementia. He had been admitted to hospital at least ten times over the past year. He was doubly incontinent and had day-night disorientation. He no longer recognised some of his family members.

Bob and his wife had been struggling to manage at home despite the support of carers. Bob had lost the mental capacity to make decisions about his care, but he had previously set up a lasting power of attorney for health and welfare and discussed his wishes regarding the future with his family and his GP.

Bob's ability to swallow started to deteriorate and he was admitted to hospital several times with aspiration pneumonia. A best interests' meeting was held with his wife and his medical and nursing team. His wife initially felt overwhelmed by the situation but she felt well supported by the team looking after her husband.

It was decided to allow Bob to comfort feed with the accepted risk of aspiration. His medication regimen was simplified. It was also felt that the best place for him to be cared for was in a nursing-home environment. The family understood that his prognosis was poor and that his life expectancy was in the region of weeks to months. He was eligible for fast-track funding, which smoothed the administrative process.

Bob's GP was informed of the plans, his details were put on the "end-of-life register" and he was discharged to a nursing home after a few weeks. His wife was able to visit him daily. Three months later he died peacefully in the nursing home surrounded by his family and friends.

Bob's family had initially felt guilty regarding the decision to care for him in a nursing home but in retrospect this felt like it had been the right decision for both Bob and his family as it had allowed them to spend quality time with him at the end of his life.

Simply important

Those simple things include time spent with friends and family who are so precious to us.

Sadly, the very fact that we are human means that our family relationships, even the most loving and supportive, are often a little messy and complicated.

In his book *The Four Things That Matter Most: a book about living*, Ira Byock, an American palliative care physician, describes the importance of being able to say to loved ones: "Please forgive me", "I forgive you", "Thank you" and "I love you". These short phrases are vital in helping us complete relationships with our families and friends. Yet they can often require determination and preparation in order to say them. "Once you've said those things, often you are able then to say 'good-bye' whenever the good-bye has to happen," says Byock.

Added to this, the ability to forgive yourself is key to a peaceful death. We will all have committed acts that we wish we hadn't and said words that we wish had remained unspoken, which may even date back to childhood, but deep down there is a yearning to put things right. In some cases, this may be straightforward; in others, contact has been lost and then we are left with our own feelings of guilt.

In situations like this, talking things through with a spiritual adviser or chaplain can be helpful. For Catholics, an opportunity to celebrate the sacrament of reconciliation, even when there may have been little contact with the Church for many years, can be a very healing process.

Talking about the illness

Talking with friends and acquaintances about the illness itself and how you are feeling can be very difficult. Often friends and neighbours don't know what to say and therefore avoid contact. This can sometimes feel like rejection and isolation. It can sometimes be helpful to overtly give them permission to talk about the illness with phrases like, "It's OK to talk about it." Sometimes if the person who is ill just acknowledges that there are no words to express how they are feeling and says that out loud, it can be enough to let others know they are not intruding, and it will break that barrier of silence sufficiently to enable the conversation to focus on everyday topics and banter.

Talking to children and grandchildren is often one of the things we fear most. We normally do all we can to protect them from sadness and upset. Yet it is important that they have an opportunity to understand what is happening and feel able to voice their own emotions.

Children are often very intuitive when something is wrong. They will pick up on sudden silences and will feel bewildered and insecure by being excluded.

When illness is explained to very young children they may initially be very sad but within a few minutes they will often have reverted to their prior activity.

Older children may respond in more complex ways. Just like adults, they may display a range of emotions. Even more so than adults, they can be caught in a space where they feel that they have to behave in a mature and adult way and not show emotion, or that they have to be strong for the other family members and younger children. It is important that they are given permission to grieve and that it is explained to them that it is normal and not something to hide or be ashamed of.

It is often helpful to inform teachers, tutors and others with a responsibility for young people's well-being of their hobbies or favourite activities so that they can be aware of when they may need some additional support and be alert to behaviour changes that may flag that they are not coping as well as they may appear to be on the surface.

Although it might be assumed that they will talk to their friends, unless those friends have themselves experienced loss, they may avoid the subject altogether.

Adolescents may well explore information themselves on the internet and turn to social media for support. There are a number of support organisations that can help them both during the time of your illness and also afterwards during bereavement. Knowing that they are not alone in their feelings is very valuable.

Living with terminal illness

Jenny was a single mother in her thirties when she developed stomach pains. After multiple investigations and medical opinions she was diagnosed with a rare form of cancer. The wait for the results was agonising, and even then there was uncertainty as to whether an operation might be possible after the initial chemotherapy. Usually a determined, independent character, Jenny wanted to be in control of her own future.

Jenny wanted facts, not uncertainty. She was devastated and angry at the situation in which she now found herself, so angry that she could not look any of the medical team in the eye. She was going to fight for her own future and that of her young child.

Jenny decided to involve her daughter in her care and was open with her about the diagnosis and treatments, using language that her toddler could understand. When Jenny had scans, the X-ray staff allowed Teddy to have a CT scan too.

Sadly the cancer did not shrink enough to enable surgery to take place and it was clear that a cure would never be possible. Jenny was frightened about what palliative care might mean. She was worried about being surrounded by the elderly and dying.

After meetings with the palliative care team in the hospital, in her own home and then in the hospice itself, Jenny began to engage and accept help. She stopped fighting the cancer and elected to make the most of every day she was living alongside it.

Despite the turmoil of her situation she started to make plans for her child's future and for when she became more unwell, and made plans for her own funeral with the help of an independent funeral celebrant.

Jenny was now determined that people should learn from her case. She talked to healthcare students and made a video for teaching purposes. She even shared her experience with the national media.

Jenny has used her experience to leave a powerful legacy for the future. Her family are very proud of her.

Coping with your illness

The thought of leaving your loved ones behind is often the greatest sadness. The idea that you will not be there to witness certain major events or rites of passage can be hard to bear. For some people, it can be helpful to consider marking these in some way, maybe writing a letter to be opened on the day with the advice you imagined yourself giving or wishes for the step they are taking.

It can also be helpful for you to write about yourself, including little things that seem so insignificant but that form part of your own history. These are the answers to the questions we never thought to ask our parents at the time when we could have done so.

What was the first record you bought? What did you enjoy most at school? What made you fall in love with your spouse? How did you propose? What was the first book you read to your child? These and many other ideas will come to you.

Sometimes being given a shorter prognosis than what we might have expected as our normal life expectancy can focus our priorities in life. For some people, it is helpful to write a bucket list of hopes and aspirations, whether that be flying a Spitfire, visiting the Sistine Chapel in Rome or seeing a West End show.

There is much to be gained by setting short-term achievable goals for what you are able realistically to do now, rather than thinking of a more ambitious plan in the hope that your condition improves. If you get to do some of the things more than once, so much the better!

Dying well

While we all hope for a good death, what this means will vary from individual to individual, although there will often be common themes. For some it will be to have all their symptoms managed well in a quiet environment. For others, it will be to have experienced life to the full and to be present for every moment possible, even if that means experiencing some symptoms, such as pain.

There is no doubt that the dying process remains a mystery. None of us knows with certainty what happens at the point of death or immediately afterwards.

However, our experience of seeing many people die suggests that there is not only a physical transition from life to death but also an emotional and spiritual one.

As the body gradually shuts down people may lapse in and out of consciousness. Sometimes it seems they are "in another world". They may be talking to a long-deceased relative or using metaphors about returning home that may often be influenced by their religious or cultural tradition. Sometimes people may speak of God or angels. At other times, they may describe more of a feeling of peace and great joy.

What does seem to be a common theme, however, is that once a person has experienced a period of agitation they often become very much more peaceful and their need for pain-relieving or anxiety-relieving medication may lessen.

Dying, God and prayer

Occasionally, well-meaning friends may suggest that the illness is part of God's will. This may be a very hard concept to grasp. Surely a loving God would not will the sadness and loss that is associated with your illness? It is not uncommon to be angry with God, at the situation, at others. We cannot fully understand the mysteries of God; however, trust that by being open to him in prayer, he will give you the strength to live your life to the fullest, with the promise of eternal life through death.

In the words of Pope Francis (from a 2013 interview in *La Republica* translated by Kathryn Wallace):

> "God is the light that illuminates the darkness, even if it does not dissolve it, and a spark of divine light is within each of us."

It is sometimes right to say no to burdensome treatment

Martin was a man in his early fifties, happily married and with a teenage daughter. Over a period of just six weeks, he developed difficulty in swallowing, lost two stone in weight and was diagnosed with a very aggressive cancer of the oesophagus which had spread to his liver. Surgery was not possible and he was offered palliative chemotherapy in the hope of improving his symptoms and extending his life expectancy. He received one treatment but his condition deteriorated due to a combination of the treatment side effects and the underlying cancer.

Although other treatment options were available, he talked with his family and decided not to have any other treatments that ran the risk of side effects as he wished to be remembered as an active father, not as "someone who is ill". His faith and the prayerful support of his family and the church community helped him make this decision.

Although clinical teams will often recommend medical interventions, especially when people are young and otherwise fit, the medical teams were very supportive of Martin's choice as it was so clearly right for him: he was at peace. He also chose to spend his last days in a hospice where family and friends were able to be with him when he died, just three months after his symptoms began.

The memories of his hands-on role as a husband and father will always live on.

Prayer can often be difficult in these times. Brian Noble, Bishop Emeritus of Shrewsbury, advises: "Pray as you can, not as you can't."

It is not uncommon in the early days following the diagnosis of a life-limiting condition for prayers to be focused on recovery, on the possibility that the medical team might have made a mistake or on the hope that the proposed treatment will have a remarkable or curative effect. Few of us wish to die and leave our loved ones behind, and so we pray for a miracle.

However, taking a step back, we see small miracles every day as people reach an understanding or acceptance of their condition or experience a precious moment with a family or friend within which they feel whole or fully human.
It is through these graced experiences
that we are made whole again.

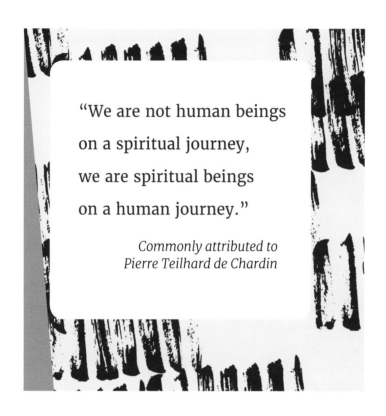

"We are not human beings
on a spiritual journey,
we are spiritual beings
on a human journey."

Commonly attributed to
Pierre Teilhard de Chardin

3

For those who care

> "He was my North, my South, my East and West,
>
> My working week and my Sunday rest,
>
> My noon, my midnight, my talk, my song.
>
> I thought that love would last forever; I was wrong..."
>
> *W.H. Auden*

When a close friend or family member is diagnosed with a life-limiting condition, for most people it will come as devastating news.

Your assumptions of growing older together may feel cruelly snatched away. There will be sadness not only for your loved one and the journey they will need to travel but also for yourself and those dear to you, for the loss of the future you had hoped and planned for.

It is true that life will not be the same again, but it does go on, and a "new normal" needs to be established, however hard that may seem at the time.

Each person may experience a number of stages of grief similar to those described in the previous chapter, yet they will be different to those experienced by the person with the illness, particularly as the physical manifestations of the illness will not be felt in the same way. We can never truly know how another is feeling.

There will be many conversations that need to take place as well as practical decisions and preparations made for when the person is less well, for when they are actively dying and, indeed, for the time after their death. These will take time and can only be approached gradually. Everyone deals with significant information in their own way and at their own speed. This can sometimes lead to anxiety and even conflict within families, especially if people do not seem to accept the news or do not wish to talk about it.

It is important to recognise that people may avoid serious conversations for fear of causing upset. While it is important to respect people's wishes and privacy, it is equally important to voice your need to talk at a deeper level, either with the person who is ill or with other family and friends or maybe the medical team. All too often we see barriers being built up, blocking communication between families, in a vain attempt to protect someone from the sadness or hurt that results from the reality of the situation. In practice, that person is often already feeling those emotions, but by putting on a brave face, they are making the situation even worse. In the words of Lesley Fallowfield, a psycho-oncologist, "Truth may hurt but deceit hurts more" (*Palliative Medicine*, 2002, July 16 (4): 297–303).

Ideally you should aim for a situation where everyone is able to be honest about how they feel and can talk about their hopes and their fears. In this way, you will all support each other. Allowing someone to tell their story can be healing for the individual and a privilege for those who are listening.

Sometimes you may find it easier to talk than at other times, but don't forget to use methods of non-verbal communication too. A hug, for those who are comfortable being touched, can say so much. This may simply not be possible, and the individual's preferences must be accommodated within the limits of the illness.

As the carer, it will be helpful for you to understand the illness and the likely course it will take. Most healthcare professionals will welcome patients bringing a close relative with them to consultations because living with a life-limiting illness really is a team effort.

Often the natural response is to try to do everything for the person affected, yet it may actually help more to encourage them to live life as normally as possible and continue the roles and tasks they have been accustomed to doing, for as long as they are able to do so.

While your loved one is reasonably well, it can be helpful to plan together how to use the time left in the best possible way. By sharing goals, it can draw you closer together. As described in the previous chapter, make opportunities to say those four important phrases to each other: *thank you, forgive me, I forgive you* and *I love you.*

Healing comes in different forms

Personal story…

Jo was a gentleman in his seventies who was diagnosed with lung cancer. He had undergone chemotherapy and was being reviewed in the clinic. His CT scans were showing a worsening of his cancer and on each visit you could see the evidence of the disease affecting his body as he grew weaker and lost muscle and weight.

Despite having this progression explained to them, Jo and his wife seemed to refuse to believe the evidence in front of them. This man who looked to be in the last few days of his life was adamant he would be recovered well enough to go on a coach holiday later that month.

When challenged, they shared their belief and said that they were praying for healing and were sure that God would answer their prayers and reverse the situation.

The doctor was concerned that despite having shared so much, they were depriving each other of the opportunity to say goodbye. She therefore gently challenged them regarding ways in which God can heal and give grace.

It is always difficult to know how such conversations are received, yet the doctor was heartened when a few days later she received a message from Jo's wife inviting her to a concert at which Jo hoped to sing for a last time.

Sadly the doctor was unable to attend due to work commitments, but she phoned them on that day. Jo was too unwell now, but they had both come to a level of acceptance where they were able to let go of "doing" and just "be". This couple who loved each other could celebrate that within the context of God's love as Jo passed away peacefully at home.

Visitors

When members of the local community hear that someone is unwell they will often try to rally round and offer support by visiting. While these visits may be very welcome, it is important to recognise just how tiring they can be both for you and for your loved one. It is natural to offer hospitality, yet this can itself be a pressure on you. Don't be afraid of asking people just to stay for ten or fifteen minutes: if your loved one really wishes them to stay longer, he or she can always ask them to do so when they make to leave.

Practical helpers

Others may offer more practical support. Some may welcome the opportunity to perform a helpful task rather than visiting as they may struggle with their own response to illness. Such practical tasks may include shopping for everyday essentials such as milk or bread; arranging or watering flowers sent by friends; making a cake to offer visitors or a meal that you can heat up yourself. Some may be prepared to provide a telephone or email update to a group of contacts to limit the number of phone calls of support you might otherwise receive on a daily basis.

As a rule, most people genuinely do wish to help although they do not always know how best to help or fear treading on someone else's toes. Within certain boundaries it may be right to accept that help, even if it goes against the grain.

More complex support

There will come a time when the person's physical or mental fitness deteriorates and professional help may be required for tasks such as washing and dressing or for more complex issues to do with symptom control or other complications. This can sometimes be a worrying time for families as your loved one may seem to be becoming "a patient".

You should feel able to ask the healthcare professionals how you can be involved in these tasks if you so wish.

It is not uncommon for there to be periods of frustration with health and social care systems in terms of either the amount of care they are able to provide or the timeliness of that care. Sometimes, despite people's best efforts, it is not how or where you or your loved one would choose to have been looked after. Communication between all parties is now key to ensure the correct priorities are met.

Some illnesses, particularly those that affect the brain or nervous system, may result in a change of personality or in emotional mood swings. The person you have always known to be kind, patient and generous may become irritable, short tempered and self-centred. This can be very hard for those around them to experience. It is essential to remember that it is the illness causing the change, not that they are rejecting you.

Touch in care

The importance of touch should not be underestimated and yet in the setting of old age or illness it may be avoided or else becomes a task for a professional carer.

There are many reasons why a person's physical appearance might change, all of which can lead to embarrassment either for themselves or for those caring for them.

Yet for them as human beings used to being in relationship with others, the isolation felt by that loss of personal touch can be devastating.

It can be helpful to create opportunities that will specifically lead to touch, such as giving your loved one a manicure or pedicure incorporating some massage, or helping them with a wet shave even when an electric razor might be easier. These small gestures may be an understated way of sharing and expressing love, and the benefit of feeling clean and well-groomed gives everyone a moment of confidence and pleasure.

Being a carer

Caring for a loved one can be all-consuming. It can be a huge privilege but may also be accompanied by feelings of overwhelming fatigue, duty, guilt or a need to prove oneself to be capable and strong, and it can go on for longer than we might imagine.

When your family member is in hospital or unwell, attention will naturally be focused on them. People do not always realise the burden the carer is carrying. Not only are you supporting the ill person, you are also supporting other family members, running the household and possibly still trying to hold down a day job.

Yet everyone asks, "How is he/she?" Rarely are you, as the carer, asked, "How are you with all of this?"

It isn't that you want the attention, yet it is important that you pause and recognise the impact that it is having on you. Ideally, you might have a confidante with whom to voice your own, often unspoken, fears of what the future holds and so on. It may be helpful to talk about how you will cope when he/she gets more ill; about whom you wish to be involved in their care when that time comes; and about your own emotions and responses to the illness, however rational or irrational they might be. That person may not be able to "fix" how you are feeling, but simply acknowledging your feelings can relieve tension and encourage you in the time ahead.

Recharge your batteries

When caring around the clock for someone, our own "quiet times" may disappear due to the work of caring and the exhaustion that leads to. However, all of us need a time to rest and recharge our batteries, physically, socially and spiritually. This time needs to be actively planned or it will be neglected. Once it is neglected, you run the risk of becoming burnt out, both physically and emotionally, and unable to care for your loved one. Looking after yourself in this way does not necessarily mean taking a week-long holiday; more often it might be arranging for somebody to sit with your loved one while you take two hours to pop to the supermarket, or maybe meet a friend for coffee outside the house or have a brief walk in a local park or along the river.

Maintaining your spiritual well-being is important too. Attendance at your weekly Mass or Sunday worship or prayer group will remind you not only of God's love and care for you, but also of the love and care you receive from the faith community you live in.

A world without him, from Barbara

He was fifty-seven when, in his words, he moved from the kingdom of the well into the kingdom of the sick. And he never crossed back. The diagnosis was devastating and absolute, without hope. And during consultations we learned to expect bad news, and that's what we got. But I was a willing companion on this journey. We'd planned a life together, forever, and even if this forever was now counted in weeks, I would be with him on that alien terrain.

The clinicians dealt with us with kindness and compassion, despite the challenge of caring for a colleague and peer. You see, he was an academic GP and an advocate for the person inside the patient. And their role was to reveal to him, this person inside the doctor, his own mortality.

For him, a fit, half-marathon-running man and invincible father of four, running was always his "thing", his time for reflection when, in his head, he wrote his scholarly articles, and put the world to rights. But when his pain was over I was the one who would have to keep running, this time alone, and as a long-distance runner. The metaphor is rich. I'd never liked running, and it was time for me to change tack.

But I loved swimming, and that's been my salvation. You can think and reminisce when the water envelops you. It's almost spiritual. And nobody can see when you cry in goggles! Underwater you are untouchable and unreachable. Except to those you want to reach out to, and that is where I find him.

Now, eight years on, I still miss him beyond words and miss the future we had planned together. I looked to forge a different future, trying out new things, but soon realised that I was more content doing the things we did together, but solo. Not trying to be the person I'm not. But I have learned to live in a world without him.

And that's my message. Find a special space where you know you will find their voice. Learn to live in a world without them. And be comfortable in your solitude.

When death happens

Ultimately there will come a time when your loved one reaches the end of their life. Hopefully you will have had an opportunity to consider how you would wish things to be at this time so that when it happens, the correct support is in place for you all.

You may feel pain, sadness and even shock. At other times, you may experience a sense of relief that your loved one will soon be at peace and free from suffering. Occasionally we may experience some unforeseen and unplanned emotions. Alfred Lord Tennyson, considering the death of a friend, reflected, "'Tis better to have loved and lost than never to have loved at all." While such sentiments may offer comfort in years to come, the immediate feelings of loss can be overwhelming.

After a death, there are several practical tasks to be performed, such as registering the death, making funeral arrangements and informing statutory bodies.

However, this is also a time to be gentle with yourself. Give yourself time to reflect on how you are feeling, on the things you are grateful for and also the hurts you are bearing. If there are things that you wish you had said to your loved one, say them now. You are entering a new phase of your life. It may feel as though a huge part of you has been taken away. The future may feel uncertain. In the spirit of Mary Ward's 1616 letter from Spa, "Without fear or anxiety, expect in the quiet confidence that God's will, will emerge in the confusion." You will always be supported.

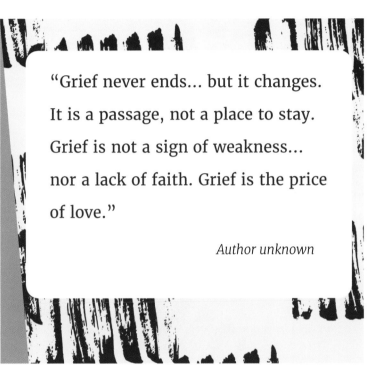

"Grief never ends... but it changes. It is a passage, not a place to stay. Grief is not a sign of weakness... nor a lack of faith. Grief is the price of love."

Author unknown

Prayers

Prayer for Holy Rest

May he support us all the day long, till the
shades lengthen and the evening comes, and
the busy world is hushed, and the fever of life
is over, and our work is done. Then in his mercy
may he give us a safe lodging, and a holy rest
and peace at the last.

John Henry Newman

Prayer for Inner Peace and Strength

O Father,
Your life in me brings stillness to my turmoil.
Your life in me brings clarity to my confusion.
Your life in me brings wisdom to my worry.
Your life in me brings contentment to my striving.
Your life in me brings gentleness to my anger.
Your life in me brings patience to my panic.
Your life in me brings hope to my suffering.
Your life in me brings faith to my frustration.
Your life in me brings such heavenly treasure into my heart
And enables me to navigate a peaceful path.
In you I find strength for my journey.

(www.living-prayers.com)

Preparation for Death

Behold me, my God, ready to embrace the death
you have destined for me. From this moment
I accept it. O my Jesus, I unite the suffering
of my death to the pain and agony which you,
my Saviour, endured in your death.

I accept the time, whether it be soon,
or after many years. I accept the manner,
whether with warning or suddenly.
In everything, I resign myself to your will.
Give me strength to suffer all with patience.

I thank you, my God, for the gift of faith.
I thank you for my many lights and graces
with which you have drawn me to your love.

I do not deserve to hear those words:
"Well done, good and faithful servant:
enter the joy of your Lord."

But your death gives me hope
that I shall be admitted to heaven,
to love you eternally, and with all my being.

I love you with all my heart;
I love you more than myself.
Grant that I may love you always,
then do with me what you will.

Holy Mary, Mother of God, pray for me
now and at the hour of my death.
Jesus, Mary and Joseph be with me
at the hour of my death.

St Alphonsus

Prayer of St Teresa of Ávila

Let nothing disturb you,

Let nothing frighten you,

All things are passing away:

God never changes.

Patience obtains all things

Whoever has God lacks nothing;

God alone suffices.

St Teresa of Ávila

Numbers 6:24–26

The Lord bless you
and keep you;
the Lord make his face to shine upon you,
and be gracious to you;
the Lord lift up his countenance upon you,
and give you peace.

Fruit-Gathering, verse 79

Let me not pray to be sheltered from dangers but to be fearless in facing them.

Let me not beg for the stilling of my pain but for the heart to conquer it.

Let me not look for allies in life's battlefield but to my own strength.

Let me not crave in anxious fear to be saved but hope for the patience to win my freedom.

Grant that I may not be a coward, feeling your mercy in my success alone, but let me find the grasp of your hand in my failure.

Rabindranath Tagore

Romans 8:38–39

For I am convinced that neither death, nor life, nor angels, nor rulers, nor things present, nor things to come, nor powers, nor height, nor depth, nor anything else in all creation, will be able to separate us from the love of God in Christ Jesus our Lord.

Psalm 121: a song of ascents

I lift up my eyes to the hills—

from where will my help come?

My help comes from the Lord,

who made heaven and earth.

He will not let your foot be moved;

he who keeps you will not slumber.

He who keeps Israel

will neither slumber nor sleep.

The Lord is your keeper;

the Lord is your shade at your right hand.

The sun shall not strike you by day,

nor the moon by night.

The Lord will keep you from all evil;

he will keep your life.

The Lord will keep

your going out and your coming in

from this time on and forevermore.

Resources

Useful websites

Dying Matters: www.dyingmatters.org

Age UK: www.ageUK.org.uk

The Art of Dying Well: www.artofdyingwell.org

Macmillan: www.macmillan.org.uk

Hospice UK: www.hospiceuk.org

NHS Choices: www.nhs.uk

Further reading

Being Mortal, Atul Gawande
(Profile Books, 2014)

With the End in Mind, Kathryn Mannix
(HarperCollins, 2017)

The Four Things that Matter Most, Ira Byock
(Simon and Schuster, 2014)

On Death and Dying, Elisabeth Kübler-Ross
(The Macmillan Company, 1969)

Hope and Grace, Monika Renz
(Jessica Kingsley Publishers, 2016)